Level 3
High-Beginner

DREAMWORKS

PUSS IN BOOTS

THE GOLD OF SAN RICARDO

Popcorn
ELT
Readers

Meet ...
everyone from PUSS IN BOOTS

Puss is from the town of San Ricardo but he does not live there now.

Humpty was Puss's friend when they were young. They lived in an orphanage. It was a home for children.

Kitty is a friend of Humpty's. She's very good at stealing things.

Puss In Boots

Humpty Dumpty

Kitty Softpaws

The Commandante

The **Comandante** and his men are from San Ricardo.

Mother Goose

the beanstalk

Jack and Jill

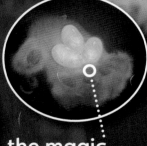

Jack and **Jill** have the magic beans. The beans grow into a very big beanstalk.

The Golden Goose has golden eggs.

the magic beans

Before you read ...
What do you think? Who lives at the top of the beanstalk?

The Golden Goose

New Words

What do these new words mean? Ask your teacher or use your dictionary.

cart

This is a **cart**.

bank

She works in a **bank**.

destroy

The wind **destroyed** the town.

bridge

The **bridge** is very old.

gold

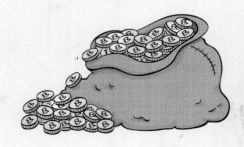

There is a lot of **gold** in the bag.

grow

It **grows** very quickly.

lock

It's a strong **lock**.

plan

Let's make a **plan**!

prison

He's in **prison**.

steal

She's **stealing** the man's bag.

'Hooray!'

Hooray!

Verbs

Present	Past
break	broke
fall	fell
grow	grew

PUSS IN BOOTS
THE GOLD OF SAN RICARDO

CHAPTER ONE
A great plan

It was a dark night. Puss In Boots ran quickly through the town. He jumped up to a window and looked in. Yes, they were there! Jack, Jill and …

'The magic beans!' Puss said quietly.

Suddenly a black cat came to the window. She jumped in quickly. Did she want the beans too?

'Hey, you!' shouted Puss.

But Jack and Jill saw him. 'Go away!' they shouted.

Puss and the black cat ran away. 'Those magic beans were mine!' he shouted.

The black cat stopped and looked at him. She was beautiful.

'Who are you?' Puss asked.

'I'm Kitty Softpaws,' she said.

There was someone behind her in the dark.

'Puss, my old friend!' said Humpty Dumpty.

'Oh no!' said Puss. 'What do YOU want?'

'Don't be angry with me,' said Humpty. 'Listen, I have a plan. Kitty is good at stealing and you are very strong. We can steal the magic beans from Jack and Jill. Then we can find the golden eggs. We're going to be very rich!'

'No!' said Puss. He walked away.

Kitty ran after him.

'Come with us, Puss,' she said.

'Do you know the story of Humpty and me?'
Puss asked.

Kitty was quiet.

'When I was young, Humpty was my friend.
Sometimes we were bad. We liked stealing
things. When I was older, I stopped stealing ...
but Humpty didn't.

'One dark night I was in bed at the orphanage.
Suddenly Humpty came in my room.

'Wake up, Puss!' he shouted. 'Come with me!'

'I ran after him. Humpty jumped into an old
cart.

'Where are we going?' I asked. Humpty did not answer.

'Wait for me here!' he said.

'Soon Humpty jumped back into the cart. He had bags of gold. We were at the San Ricardo bank!

'No, Humpty!' I said. 'This is the gold of the people!'

'I wanted to take the gold back. But the Comandante and his men came after us. We went quickly. On the bridge out of the town, the cart broke. CRASH! The cart and the gold fell into the water.

'Help me!' Humpty shouted.

'I did not help him. I jumped into the water. Humpty went to prison.'

Puss looked at Kitty. 'After that I had no home and no friends in San Ricardo.'

Humpty walked up to Puss again.

'I'm sorry,' he said. 'It was bad of me. But we can give the gold back to the people of San Ricardo. They can have the golden eggs. It's a great plan, Puss!'

Puss was quiet.

'OK,' he said. 'For the people of San Ricardo, but not for you. We are NOT friends.'

CHAPTER TWO
The Golden Goose

Puss and Kitty waited next to the road for Jack and Jill's cart.

'Now!' shouted Kitty.

They jumped onto the cart. The magic beans were inside.

Kitty opened the lock quickly. 'Take the beans,' she said.

'Wow!' Puss said.

Suddenly Jill saw Puss and Kitty. 'Stop!' she shouted.

But Humpty came with his cart.

'Jump on!' Humpty laughed. 'Now we've got the magic beans!'

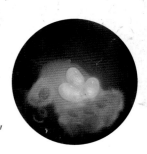

Soon Humpty stopped the cart. 'This is the place! Put the beans here!' he said.

Puss put the beans down. A beanstalk started to grow.

'It's very small,' said Humpty.

Suddenly the beanstalk grew up and up. 'Quick!' shouted Humpty. 'Jump on!'

It was beautiful at the top of the beanstalk.

'Look!' shouted Kitty. There were golden eggs everywhere.

'How are we going to take the eggs home?' asked Puss.

Then they saw the Golden Goose.

'We don't need these eggs,' said Humpty. 'We can take the Golden Goose!'

There was a terrible noise behind them.
'What's that?' asked Puss.
They started to run.
'Quick!' shouted Humpty. 'Take the Golden Goose down the beanstalk!'

That night everyone was happy. They had a lot of golden eggs from the Golden Goose. Puss and Kitty danced.

'Listen, Puss,' she said quietly. 'Don't stay here.'

'Why?' answered Puss. 'I want to stay with you and Humpty.'

'It's late!' shouted Humpty. 'See you in the morning. Goodnight!'

'Goodnight, Humpty!' said Puss.

But when he went to sleep, he did not look behind him ...

CHAPTER THREE
Prison

Next morning when Puss opened his eyes, there was no one there. No Kitty, no Humpty, no Golden Goose.

'Jack and Jill were here. I know it!' thought Puss. 'They have got my friends!'

There was only one place to find Humpty and Kitty – San Ricardo.

San Ricardo was very quiet. Where was everyone? Then Puss saw Jack and Jill with Humpty.

'Stop!' Puss shouted, but they all laughed at him.

'What about our plan?' asked Puss.

'This IS the plan!' said Humpty.

'I don't understand,' said Puss. 'Are you friends with Jack and Jill now?'

'Oh, yes,' said Humpty. 'And now all the people of San Ricardo are my friends too. Look! They all have golden eggs.'

Humpty was angry now. 'You ran away from me when I was on the bridge!' he shouted. 'This time YOU are going to prison! Comandante, take him!'

It was cold and dark in prison. Puss was very sad. 'I am not a bad cat,' he thought.

Suddenly Kitty looked in the door. She opened the lock quickly.

'A good friend is better than gold,' she said.

'Thanks!' said Puss. 'Now we have to stop Humpty!'

CHAPTER FOUR
'San Ricardo is our home!'

Humpty had the Golden Goose in his arms.

'What's the plan now, Humpty?' said Puss. He was angry.

There was a terrible noise again. This time it was not very far away.

'What's that?' Puss asked.

'That is Mother Goose!' said Humpty. 'She wants the Golden Goose back. When she comes, she's going to destroy San Ricardo. And then all the golden eggs are mine!'

'Humpty,' said Puss, 'don't do this. San Ricardo is our home. We can stop Mother Goose and we can be friends again.'

Humpty was quiet.

'OK, Puss,' he said. 'It's good to be friends.'

Mother Goose was very big. The people of San Ricardo ran away from her.

Humpty went out of the town with the Golden Goose on his cart.

'Mother Goose,' shouted Puss. 'Look!'

Mother Goose saw the Golden Goose and ran to the bridge. But she was very big and the bridge broke under her. Humpty and the Golden Goose were on the bridge ...

'Humpty! I'm coming!' shouted Puss.

'No!' said Humpty. 'Don't help me! Help the Golden Goose!'

Humpty fell and broke. There was a golden egg inside him.

Puss was sad. 'My friend,' he said, 'you were good inside.'

Mother Goose and the Golden Goose went back home.

In San Ricardo, the people were very happy. 'We have our gold again!' they shouted. 'Hooray for Puss In Boots!'

THE END

Real World

GOLD

Everyone is looking for gold in Puss In Boots. But how much do you know about gold?

Where does gold come from?

- Today gold comes from mines in many different countries. A lot of gold comes from China, Australia, the USA, Russia, South Africa and Peru. Many rivers have gold in them, for example, the Amazon River in South America or the Colorado River in the USA.

RUSSIA

THE USA

CHINA

Amazon River

PERU

AUSTRALIA

SOUTH AFRICA

When did people first find gold?

- No one knows, but we know people had gold about 4,500 years ago.
- The famous Egyptian mask of Tutankhamun is gold and it is more than 3,000 years old.
- The first gold money is about 2,500 years old.

What can we do with gold today?

- Gold is an electrical conductor. Every mobile phone and TV has some gold in it.
- This space helmet has gold on it. The gold can protect a person's face from very strong sun.

DID YOU KNOW?

Gold is very expensive so this Olympic gold medal is only 1.34 % gold!

London 2012

⭐ **Do you have anything gold?** ⭐

What do these words mean? Find out.

mine   electrical conductor
mobile phone   protect   expensive

After you read

1 Match the people and descriptions.

a) She was very big.
b) Her eggs were golden.
c) The people loved him.
d) He was good inside.
e) They had the magic beans.

i) Jack and Jill
ii) Humpty
iii) Mother Goose
iv) Puss In Boots
v) The Golden Goose

2 Complete the sentences with the verbs in the box.

broke   grew   opened   ran   saw   ~~waited~~   went

a) Puss and Kitty ....**waited**... for Jack and Jill's cart.
b) The beanstalk ....
c) Humpty .... down the beanstalk with the Golden Goose.
d) Puss .... Humpty with Jack and Jill.
e) Kitty .... the prison door.
f) The people .... away from Mother Goose.
g) Humpty fell and ....

Where's the popcorn?
Look in your book.
Can you find it?

Puzzle time!

1 Find the letters and spell a word from the story.

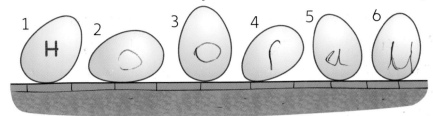

1 This was Puss's friend when he was young. Write the first letter of his name.

2 Write the second letter of this word.

3 What's in the bag? Write the second letter of this word.

4 What's this? Write the third letter of this word.

5 What's this? Write the third letter of this word.

6 This is Humpty's new friend. Write the last letter of her name.

2 Answer the questions.

a) If all the golden eggs are the same, how many kilograms is one egg? ....

b) If the green egg is 1000g, how many kilograms is one golden egg? ....

3 Look at the pictures and complete the sentences.

A  B  C

a) Beanstalk B is yellow because there is no ....

b) Beanstalk C is not growing because it has no
   ....

c) Beanstalk .... is growing well.

d) Beans need .... and ....

4a Did you like the story? Write your name in box 1 and colour the stars. Now ask five friends.

★★★
Yes, it was great!

★★☆
Yes, I liked it!

★☆☆
It was quite good.

☆☆☆
No, I didn't like it.

Name				Name			
1	☆	☆	☆	4	☆	☆	☆
2	☆	☆	☆	5	☆	☆	☆
3	☆	☆	☆	6	☆	☆	☆

b Complete the sentence with *everyone*, *some of us* or *no one*.

.... liked the story.

Imagine...

1 Choose one of the characters.

Puss In Boots

Humpty Dumpty

Kitty Softpaws

2 What does your character do in the story? Think of one thing. Mime it for your friends. Can your friends guess what you are doing?

Are you dancing?

No, I'm not!

Are you going up the beanstalk?

Yes, I am!

Chant

1 Listen and read.

The gold of San Ricardo

Humpty had a plan,
He wanted to be rich.
'Listen, Puss,' he said. 'I want
The gold of San Ricardo!'

Puss jumped in the water,
He did not help his friend.
'No!' he said. 'We cannot steal
The gold of San Ricardo!'

The people saw the Golden Goose,
With her golden eggs.
'Look!' they said. 'Here it is!
The gold of San Ricardo!'

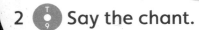

2 Say the chant.